ELEANOR HASKINS-MONAHAN

ISBN 0-7683-2098-4

Written by Flavia and Lisa Weedn
Illustrated by Flavia Weedn
© Weedn Family Trust
www.flavia.com
All rights reserved

Published in 1999 by Cedco Publishing Company
100 Pelican Way, San Rafael, California 94901
For a free catalog of other Cedco® products, please write
to the address above, or visit our website: www.cedco.com

Printed in Hong Kong

3  5  7  9  10  8  6  4

The artwork for each picture is digitally mastered using acrylic on canvas.

*With love and gratitude to those talented souls who made this book a reality—
Rick Weedn, Lisa Mansfield, Diana Musacchio, Jane Durand, Tyler Tomblin,
Heather Day, Solveig Chandler, Hui-Ying Ting-Bornfreund and Annette Berlin.*

# AN ILLUSTRATED ADDRESS BOOK

## Forever

FLAVIA AND LISA WEEDN

ILLUSTRATED BY FLAVIA WEEDN

CEDCO PUBLISHING COMPANY · SAN RAFAEL, CALIFORNIA

A

NAME:                                         HOME:

ADDRESS:                                      CELL/PAGER:

                                              OFFICE:

E-MAIL:                                       FAX:

NAME:                                         HOME:

ADDRESS:                                      CELL/PAGER:

                                              OFFICE:

E-MAIL:                                       FAX:

NAME:                                         HOME:

ADDRESS:                                      CELL/PAGER:

                                              OFFICE:

E-MAIL:                                       FAX:

NAME:                                         HOME:

ADDRESS:                                      CELL/PAGER:

                                              OFFICE:

E-MAIL:                                       FAX:

NAME:                                         HOME:

ADDRESS:                                      CELL/PAGER:

                                              OFFICE:

E-MAIL:                                       FAX:

NAME:                                    HOME:

ADDRESS:                                 CELL/PAGER:

                                         OFFICE:

E-MAIL:                                  FAX:

NAME:                                    HOME:

ADDRESS:                                 CELL/PAGER:

                                         OFFICE:

E-MAIL:                                  FAX:

NAME:                                    HOME:

ADDRESS:                                 CELL/PAGER:

                                         OFFICE:

E-MAIL:                                  FAX:

NAME:                                    HOME:

ADDRESS:                                 CELL/PAGER:

                                         OFFICE:

E-MAIL:                                  FAX:

NAME:                                    HOME:

ADDRESS:                                 CELL/PAGER:

                                         OFFICE:

E-MAIL:                                  FAX:

NAME:                                           HOME:

ADDRESS:                                         CELL/PAGER:

                                                OFFICE:

E-MAIL:                                          FAX:

NAME:                                           HOME:

ADDRESS:                                         CELL/PAGER:

                                                OFFICE:

E-MAIL:                                          FAX:

NAME:                                           HOME:

ADDRESS:                                         CELL/PAGER:

                                                OFFICE:

E-MAIL:                                          FAX:

NAME:                                           HOME:

ADDRESS:                                         CELL/PAGER:

                                                OFFICE:

E-MAIL:                                          FAX:

NAME:                                           HOME:

ADDRESS:                                         CELL/PAGER:

                                                OFFICE:

E-MAIL:                                          FAX:

WE ARE EACH A PART OF ONE ANOTHER,

CONNECTED BY THE SWEET MYSTERY OF LIFE.

NAME:                                          HOME:

ADDRESS:                                       CELL/PAGER:

                                               OFFICE:

E-MAIL:                                         FAX:

NAME:                                          HOME:

ADDRESS:                                       CELL/PAGER:

                                               OFFICE:

E-MAIL:                                         FAX:

NAME:                                          HOME:

ADDRESS:                                       CELL/PAGER:

                                               OFFICE:

E-MAIL:                                         FAX:

NAME:                                          HOME:

ADDRESS:                                       CELL/PAGER:

                                               OFFICE:

E-MAIL:                                         FAX:

NAME:                                          HOME:

ADDRESS:                                       CELL/PAGER:

                                               OFFICE:

E-MAIL:                                         FAX:

NAME:                                              HOME:

ADDRESS:                                           CELL/PAGER:

                                                   OFFICE:

E-MAIL:                                             FAX:

NAME:                                              HOME:

ADDRESS:                                           CELL/PAGER:

                                                   OFFICE:

E-MAIL:                                             FAX:

NAME:                                              HOME:

ADDRESS:                                           CELL/PAGER:

                                                   OFFICE:

E-MAIL:                                             FAX:

NAME:                                              HOME:

ADDRESS:                                           CELL/PAGER:

                                                   OFFICE:

E-MAIL:                                             FAX:

NAME:                                              HOME:

ADDRESS:                                           CELL/PAGER:

                                                   OFFICE:

E-MAIL:                                             FAX:

NAME:                                          HOME:

ADDRESS:                                        CELL/PAGER:

                                                OFFICE:

E-MAIL:                                         FAX:

NAME:                                          HOME:

ADDRESS:                                        CELL/PAGER:

                                                OFFICE:

E-MAIL:                                         FAX:

NAME:                                          HOME:

ADDRESS:                                        CELL/PAGER:

                                                OFFICE:

E-MAIL:                                         FAX:

NAME:                                          HOME:

ADDRESS:                                        CELL/PAGER:

                                                OFFICE:

E-MAIL:                                         FAX:

NAME:                                          HOME:

ADDRESS:                                        CELL/PAGER:

                                                OFFICE:

E-MAIL:                                         FAX:

THE DIVINE CAPACITY OF THE HUMAN SPIRIT

GIVES US REASON TO BELIEVE.

NAME:                                          HOME:

ADDRESS:                                       CELL/PAGER:

                                               OFFICE:

E-MAIL:                                         FAX:

NAME:                                          HOME:

ADDRESS:                                       CELL/PAGER:

                                               OFFICE:

E-MAIL:                                         FAX:

NAME:                                          HOME:

ADDRESS:                                       CELL/PAGER:

                                               OFFICE:

E-MAIL:                                         FAX:

NAME:                                          HOME:

ADDRESS:                                       CELL/PAGER:

                                               OFFICE:

E-MAIL:                                         FAX:

NAME:                                          HOME:

ADDRESS:                                       CELL/PAGER:

                                               OFFICE:

E-MAIL:                                         FAX:

NAME:                                    HOME:

ADDRESS:                                 CELL/PAGER:

                                         OFFICE:

E-MAIL:                                  FAX:

NAME:                                    HOME:

ADDRESS:                                 CELL/PAGER:

                                         OFFICE:

E-MAIL:                                  FAX:

NAME:                                    HOME:

ADDRESS:                                 CELL/PAGER:

                                         OFFICE:

E-MAIL:                                  FAX:

NAME:                                    HOME:

ADDRESS:                                 CELL/PAGER:

                                         OFFICE:

E-MAIL:                                  FAX:

NAME:                                    HOME:

ADDRESS:                                 CELL/PAGER:

                                         OFFICE:

E-MAIL:                                  FAX:

NAME:            HOME:

ADDRESS:           CELL/PAGER:

                                     OFFICE:

E-MAIL:             FAX:

NAME:            HOME:

ADDRESS:           CELL/PAGER:

                                     OFFICE:

E-MAIL:             FAX:

NAME:            HOME:

ADDRESS:           CELL/PAGER:

                                     OFFICE:

E-MAIL:             FAX:

NAME:            HOME:

ADDRESS:           CELL/PAGER:

                                     OFFICE:

E-MAIL:             FAX:

NAME:            HOME:

ADDRESS:           CELL/PAGER:

                                     OFFICE:

E-MAIL:             FAX:

TO BELIEVE IS TO HAVE FAITH,

WHICH IS TO KNOW WE ARE NEVER ALONE.

NAME:                                            HOME:

ADDRESS:                                         CELL/PAGER:

                                                 OFFICE:

E-MAIL:                                          FAX:

NAME:                                            HOME:

ADDRESS:                                         CELL/PAGER:

                                                 OFFICE:

E-MAIL:                                          FAX:

NAME:                                            HOME:

ADDRESS:                                         CELL/PAGER:

                                                 OFFICE:

E-MAIL:                                          FAX:

NAME:                                            HOME:

ADDRESS:                                         CELL/PAGER:

                                                 OFFICE:

E-MAIL:                                          FAX:

NAME:                                            HOME:

ADDRESS:                                         CELL/PAGER:

                                                 OFFICE:

E-MAIL:                                          FAX:

NAME:                                          HOME:

ADDRESS:                                        CELL/PAGER:

                                               OFFICE:

E-MAIL:                                         FAX:

NAME:                                          HOME:

ADDRESS:                                        CELL/PAGER:

                                               OFFICE:

E-MAIL:                                         FAX:

NAME:                                          HOME:

ADDRESS:                                        CELL/PAGER:

                                               OFFICE:

E-MAIL:                                         FAX:

NAME:                                          HOME:

ADDRESS:                                        CELL/PAGER:

                                               OFFICE:

E-MAIL:                                         FAX:

NAME:                                          HOME:

ADDRESS:                                        CELL/PAGER:

                                               OFFICE:

E-MAIL:                                         FAX:

NAME:

ADDRESS:

E-MAIL:

HOME:

CELL/PAGER:

OFFICE:

FAX:

NAME:

ADDRESS:

E-MAIL:

HOME:

CELL/PAGER:

OFFICE:

FAX:

NAME:

ADDRESS:

E-MAIL:

HOME:

CELL/PAGER:

OFFICE:

FAX:

NAME:

ADDRESS:

E-MAIL:

HOME:

CELL/PAGER:

OFFICE:

FAX:

NAME:

ADDRESS:

E-MAIL:

HOME:

CELL/PAGER:

OFFICE:

FAX:

IN DESTINY'S GRAND DESIGN THERE ARE
NO RANDOM MEETINGS, FOR ALL IS MEANT TO BE.

NAME:                                          HOME:

ADDRESS:                                       CELL/PAGER:

                                               OFFICE:

E-MAIL:                                         FAX:

NAME:                                          HOME:

ADDRESS:                                       CELL/PAGER:

                                               OFFICE:

E-MAIL:                                         FAX:

NAME:                                          HOME:

ADDRESS:                                       CELL/PAGER:

                                               OFFICE:

E-MAIL:                                         FAX:

NAME:                                          HOME:

ADDRESS:                                       CELL/PAGER:

                                               OFFICE:

E-MAIL:                                         FAX:

NAME:                                          HOME:

ADDRESS:                                       CELL/PAGER:

                                               OFFICE:

E-MAIL:                                         FAX:

NAME:                                          HOME:

ADDRESS:                                        CELL/PAGER:

                                                OFFICE:

E-MAIL:                                          FAX:

NAME:                                          HOME:

ADDRESS:                                        CELL/PAGER:

                                                OFFICE:

E-MAIL:                                          FAX:

NAME:                                          HOME:

ADDRESS:                                        CELL/PAGER:

                                                OFFICE:

E-MAIL:                                          FAX:

NAME:                                          HOME:

ADDRESS:                                        CELL/PAGER:

                                                OFFICE:

E-MAIL:                                          FAX:

NAME:                                          HOME:

ADDRESS:                                        CELL/PAGER:

                                                OFFICE:

E-MAIL:                                          FAX:

NAME:                                          HOME:

ADDRESS:                                       CELL/PAGER:

                                               OFFICE:

E-MAIL:                                        FAX:

NAME:                                          HOME:

ADDRESS:                                       CELL/PAGER:

                                               OFFICE:

E-MAIL:                                        FAX:

NAME:                                          HOME:

ADDRESS:                                       CELL/PAGER:

                                               OFFICE:

E-MAIL:                                        FAX:

NAME:                                          HOME:

ADDRESS:                                       CELL/PAGER:

                                               OFFICE:

E-MAIL:                                        FAX:

NAME:                                          HOME:

ADDRESS:                                       CELL/PAGER:

                                               OFFICE:

E-MAIL:                                        FAX:

SOME PEOPLE LEAVE FOOTPRINTS ON OUR HEARTS

AND WE ARE NEVER, EVER THE SAME.

F

NAME:                                          HOME:

ADDRESS:                                       CELL/PAGER:

                                               OFFICE:

E-MAIL:                                         FAX:

NAME:                                          HOME:

ADDRESS:                                       CELL/PAGER:

                                               OFFICE:

E-MAIL:                                         FAX:

NAME:                                          HOME:

ADDRESS:                                       CELL/PAGER:

                                               OFFICE:

E-MAIL:                                         FAX:

NAME:                                          HOME:

ADDRESS:                                       CELL/PAGER:

                                               OFFICE:

E-MAIL:                                         FAX:

NAME:                                          HOME:

ADDRESS:                                       CELL/PAGER:

                                               OFFICE:

E-MAIL:                                         FAX:

NAME:                                          HOME:

ADDRESS:                                       CELL/PAGER:

                                               OFFICE:

E-MAIL:                                        FAX:

NAME:                                          HOME:

ADDRESS:                                       CELL/PAGER:

                                               OFFICE:

E-MAIL:                                        FAX:

NAME:                                          HOME:

ADDRESS:                                       CELL/PAGER:

                                               OFFICE:

E-MAIL:                                        FAX:

NAME:                                          HOME:

ADDRESS:                                       CELL/PAGER:

                                               OFFICE:

E-MAIL:                                        FAX:

NAME:                                          HOME:

ADDRESS:                                       CELL/PAGER:

                                               OFFICE:

E-MAIL:                                        FAX:

NAME:                                          HOME:

ADDRESS:                                        CELL/PAGER:

                                                OFFICE:

E-MAIL:                                         FAX:

NAME:                                          HOME:

ADDRESS:                                        CELL/PAGER:

                                                OFFICE:

E-MAIL:                                         FAX:

NAME:                                          HOME:

ADDRESS:                                        CELL/PAGER:

                                                OFFICE:

E-MAIL:                                         FAX:

NAME:                                          HOME:

ADDRESS:                                        CELL/PAGER:

                                                OFFICE:

E-MAIL:                                         FAX:

NAME:                                          HOME:

ADDRESS:                                        CELL/PAGER:

                                                OFFICE:

E-MAIL:                                         FAX:

LIFE IS A PRECIOUS OFFERING,

AND LOVE IS A MIRACLE THAT BELIES THE PASSAGE OF TIME.

G

NAME:                                          HOME:

ADDRESS:                                       CELL/PAGER:

                                               OFFICE:

E-MAIL:                                         FAX:

NAME:                                          HOME:

ADDRESS:                                       CELL/PAGER:

                                               OFFICE:

E-MAIL:                                         FAX:

NAME:                                          HOME:

ADDRESS:                                       CELL/PAGER:

                                               OFFICE:

E-MAIL:                                         FAX:

NAME:                                          HOME:

ADDRESS:                                       CELL/PAGER:

                                               OFFICE:

E-MAIL:                                         FAX:

NAME:                                          HOME:

ADDRESS:                                       CELL/PAGER:

                                               OFFICE:

E-MAIL:                                         FAX:

NAME:                                    HOME:

ADDRESS:                                 CELL/PAGER:

                                         OFFICE:

E-MAIL:                                  FAX:

NAME:                                    HOME:

ADDRESS:                                 CELL/PAGER:

                                         OFFICE:

E-MAIL:                                  FAX:

NAME:                                    HOME:

ADDRESS:                                 CELL/PAGER:

                                         OFFICE:

E-MAIL:                                  FAX:

NAME:                                    HOME:

ADDRESS:                                 CELL/PAGER:

                                         OFFICE:

E-MAIL:                                  FAX:

NAME:                                    HOME:

ADDRESS:                                 CELL/PAGER:

                                         OFFICE:

E-MAIL:                                  FAX:

NAME:

ADDRESS:

E-MAIL:

HOME:

CELL/PAGER:

OFFICE:

FAX:

NAME:

ADDRESS:

E-MAIL:

HOME:

CELL/PAGER:

OFFICE:

FAX:

NAME:

ADDRESS:

E-MAIL:

HOME:

CELL/PAGER:

OFFICE:

FAX:

NAME:

ADDRESS:

E-MAIL:

HOME:

CELL/PAGER:

OFFICE:

FAX:

NAME:

ADDRESS:

E-MAIL:

HOME:

CELL/PAGER:

OFFICE:

FAX:

ALL THAT WE FEEL IN LIFE IS BORN OF LOVE'S TOUCH.

H

NAME:                                          HOME:

ADDRESS:                                        CELL/PAGER:

                                                OFFICE:

E-MAIL:                                         FAX:

NAME:                                          HOME:

ADDRESS:                                        CELL/PAGER:

                                                OFFICE:

E-MAIL:                                         FAX:

NAME:                                          HOME:

ADDRESS:                                        CELL/PAGER:

                                                OFFICE:

E-MAIL:                                         FAX:

NAME:                                          HOME:

ADDRESS:                                        CELL/PAGER:

                                                OFFICE:

E-MAIL:                                         FAX:

NAME:                                          HOME:

ADDRESS:                                        CELL/PAGER:

                                                OFFICE:

E-MAIL:                                         FAX:

NAME:                                    HOME:

ADDRESS:                                 CELL/PAGER:

                                         OFFICE:

E-MAIL:                                   FAX:

NAME:                                    HOME:

ADDRESS:                                 CELL/PAGER:

                                         OFFICE:

E-MAIL:                                   FAX:

NAME:                                    HOME:

ADDRESS:                                 CELL/PAGER:

                                         OFFICE:

E-MAIL:                                   FAX:

NAME:                                    HOME:

ADDRESS:                                 CELL/PAGER:

                                         OFFICE:

E-MAIL:                                   FAX:

NAME:                                    HOME:

ADDRESS:                                 CELL/PAGER:

                                         OFFICE:

E-MAIL:                                   FAX:

NAME:                                          HOME:

ADDRESS:                                        CELL/PAGER:

                                                OFFICE:

E-MAIL:                                          FAX:

NAME:                                          HOME:

ADDRESS:                                        CELL/PAGER:

                                                OFFICE:

E-MAIL:                                          FAX:

NAME:                                          HOME:

ADDRESS:                                        CELL/PAGER:

                                                OFFICE:

E-MAIL:                                          FAX:

NAME:                                          HOME:

ADDRESS:                                        CELL/PAGER:

                                                OFFICE:

E-MAIL:                                          FAX:

NAME:                                          HOME:

ADDRESS:                                        CELL/PAGER:

                                                OFFICE:

E-MAIL:                                          FAX:

TREASURE THE VALUE

OF PROFOUND KINSHIPS AND THE POWER OF CARE.

I

NAME:                                           HOME:

ADDRESS:                                        CELL/PAGER:

                                                OFFICE:

E-MAIL:                                         FAX:

NAME:                                           HOME:

ADDRESS:                                        CELL/PAGER:

                                                OFFICE:

E-MAIL:                                         FAX:

NAME:                                           HOME:

ADDRESS:                                        CELL/PAGER:

                                                OFFICE:

E-MAIL:                                         FAX:

NAME:                                           HOME:

ADDRESS:                                        CELL/PAGER:

                                                OFFICE:

E-MAIL:                                         FAX:

NAME:                                           HOME:

ADDRESS:                                        CELL/PAGER:

                                                OFFICE:

E-MAIL:                                         FAX:

NAME:                                          HOME:

ADDRESS:                                       CELL/PAGER:

                                               OFFICE:

E-MAIL:                                         FAX:

NAME:                                          HOME:

ADDRESS:                                       CELL/PAGER:

                                               OFFICE:

E-MAIL:                                         FAX:

NAME:                                          HOME:

ADDRESS:                                       CELL/PAGER:

                                               OFFICE:

E-MAIL:                                         FAX:

NAME:                                          HOME:

ADDRESS:                                       CELL/PAGER:

                                               OFFICE:

E-MAIL:                                         FAX:

NAME:                                          HOME:

ADDRESS:                                       CELL/PAGER:

                                               OFFICE:

E-MAIL:                                         FAX:

NAME:                                    HOME:

ADDRESS:                                 CELL/PAGER:

                                         OFFICE:

E-MAIL:                                   FAX:

NAME:                                    HOME:

ADDRESS:                                 CELL/PAGER:

                                         OFFICE:

E-MAIL:                                   FAX:

NAME:                                    HOME:

ADDRESS:                                 CELL/PAGER:

                                         OFFICE:

E-MAIL:                                   FAX:

NAME:                                    HOME:

ADDRESS:                                 CELL/PAGER:

                                         OFFICE:

E-MAIL:                                   FAX:

NAME:                                    HOME:

ADDRESS:                                 CELL/PAGER:

                                         OFFICE:

E-MAIL:                                   FAX:

HOLD CLOSE THE EVER-PRESENT BLESSING

OF THIS JOURNEY WE ALL SHARE.

J

NAME:                                          HOME:

ADDRESS:                                        CELL/PAGER:

                                                OFFICE:

E-MAIL:                                          FAX:

NAME:                                          HOME:

ADDRESS:                                        CELL/PAGER:

                                                OFFICE:

E-MAIL:                                          FAX:

NAME:                                          HOME:

ADDRESS:                                        CELL/PAGER:

                                                OFFICE:

E-MAIL:                                          FAX:

NAME:                                          HOME:

ADDRESS:                                        CELL/PAGER:

                                                OFFICE:

E-MAIL:                                          FAX:

NAME:                                          HOME:

ADDRESS:                                        CELL/PAGER:

                                                OFFICE:

E-MAIL:                                          FAX:

NAME:                                          HOME:

ADDRESS:                                        CELL/PAGER:

                                                OFFICE:

E-MAIL:                                          FAX:

NAME:                                          HOME:

ADDRESS:                                        CELL/PAGER:

                                                OFFICE:

E-MAIL:                                          FAX:

NAME:                                          HOME:

ADDRESS:                                        CELL/PAGER:

                                                OFFICE:

E-MAIL:                                          FAX:

NAME:                                          HOME:

ADDRESS:                                        CELL/PAGER:

                                                OFFICE:

E-MAIL:                                          FAX:

NAME:                                          HOME:

ADDRESS:                                        CELL/PAGER:

                                                OFFICE:

E-MAIL:                                          FAX:

NAME:                                    HOME:

ADDRESS:                                 CELL/PAGER:

                                         OFFICE:

E-MAIL:                                  FAX:

NAME:                                    HOME:

ADDRESS:                                 CELL/PAGER:

                                         OFFICE:

E-MAIL:                                  FAX:

NAME:                                    HOME:

ADDRESS:                                 CELL/PAGER:

                                         OFFICE:

E-MAIL:                                  FAX:

NAME:                                    HOME:

ADDRESS:                                 CELL/PAGER:

                                         OFFICE:

E-MAIL:                                  FAX:

NAME:                                    HOME:

ADDRESS:                                 CELL/PAGER:

                                         OFFICE:

E-MAIL:                                  FAX:

WALK LIFE'S PATH WITH GENTLE FOOTSTEPS,

WITH KINDNESS AND WITH A LISTENING HEART.

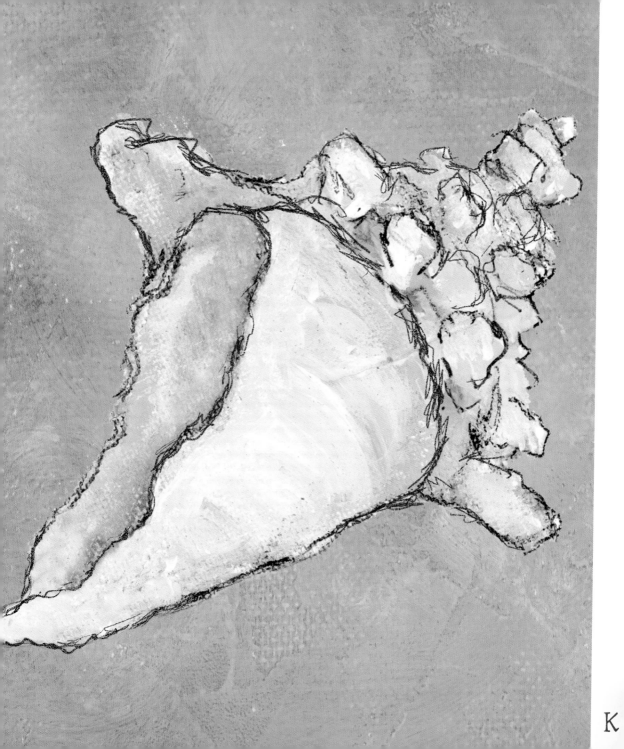

K

NAME:                                      HOME:

ADDRESS:                              CELL/PAGER:

                                            OFFICE:

E-MAIL:                                  FAX:

NAME:                                        HOME:

ADDRESS:                              CELL/PAGER:

                                            OFFICE:

E-MAIL:                                  FAX:

NAME:                                        HOME:

ADDRESS:                              CELL/PAGER:

                                            OFFICE:

E-MAIL:                                  FAX:

NAME:                                        HOME:

ADDRESS:                              CELL/PAGER:

                                            OFFICE:

E-MAIL:                                  FAX:

NAME:                                        HOME:

ADDRESS:                              CELL/PAGER:

                                            OFFICE:

E-MAIL:                                  FAX:

NAME:                                          HOME:

ADDRESS:                                       CELL/PAGER:

                                               OFFICE:

E-MAIL:                                        FAX:

NAME:                                          HOME:

ADDRESS:                                       CELL/PAGER:

                                               OFFICE:

E-MAIL:                                        FAX:

NAME:                                          HOME:

ADDRESS:                                       CELL/PAGER:

                                               OFFICE:

E-MAIL:                                        FAX:

NAME:                                          HOME:

ADDRESS:                                       CELL/PAGER:

                                               OFFICE:

E-MAIL:                                        FAX:

NAME:                                          HOME:

ADDRESS:                                       CELL/PAGER:

                                               OFFICE:

E-MAIL:                                        FAX:

NAME:                                          HOME:

ADDRESS:                                       CELL/PAGER:

                                               OFFICE:

E-MAIL:                                        FAX:

NAME:                                          HOME:

ADDRESS:                                       CELL/PAGER:

                                               OFFICE:

E-MAIL:                                        FAX:

NAME:                                          HOME:

ADDRESS:                                       CELL/PAGER:

                                               OFFICE:

E-MAIL:                                        FAX:

NAME:                                          HOME:

ADDRESS:                                       CELL/PAGER:

                                               OFFICE:

E-MAIL:                                        FAX:

NAME:                                          HOME:

ADDRESS:                                       CELL/PAGER:

                                               OFFICE:

E-MAIL:                                        FAX:

*LOVE'S GIFT IS FOREVER,*

*FOR TIME HAS NO MEANING IN MATTERS OF THE HEART.*

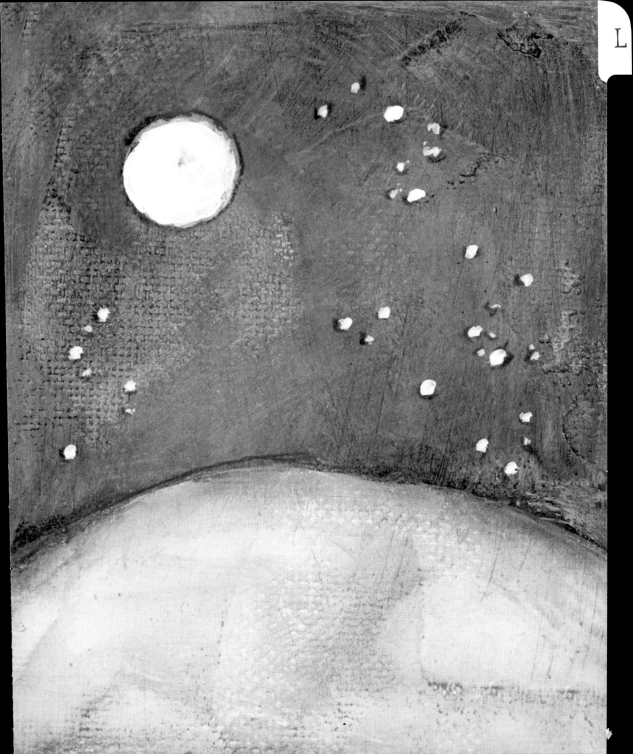

NAME:                             HOME:

ADDRESS:                       CELL/PAGER:

                                 OFFICE:

E-MAIL:                            FAX:

NAME:                             HOME:

ADDRESS:                       CELL/PAGER:

                                 OFFICE:

E-MAIL:                            FAX:

NAME:                             HOME:

ADDRESS:                       CELL/PAGER:

                                 OFFICE:

E-MAIL:                            FAX:

NAME:                             HOME:

ADDRESS:                       CELL/PAGER:

                                 OFFICE:

E-MAIL:                            FAX:

NAME:                             HOME:

ADDRESS:                       CELL/PAGER:

                                 OFFICE:

E-MAIL:                            FAX:

NAME:                                         HOME:

ADDRESS:                         CELL/PAGER:

                                      OFFICE:

E-MAIL:                           FAX:

NAME:                                           HOME:

ADDRESS:                         CELL/PAGER:

                                        OFFICE:

E-MAIL:                           FAX:

NAME:                                           HOME:

ADDRESS:                         CELL/PAGER:

                                        OFFICE:

E-MAIL:                           FAX:

NAME:                                           HOME:

ADDRESS:                         CELL/PAGER:

                                        OFFICE:

E-MAIL:                           FAX:

NAME:                                           HOME:

ADDRESS:                         CELL/PAGER:

                                        OFFICE:

E-MAIL:                           FAX:

NAME:                                          HOME:

ADDRESS:                                        CELL/PAGER:

                                               OFFICE:

E-MAIL:                                         FAX:

NAME:                                          HOME:

ADDRESS:                                        CELL/PAGER:

                                               OFFICE:

E-MAIL:                                         FAX:

NAME:                                          HOME:

ADDRESS:                                        CELL/PAGER:

                                               OFFICE:

E-MAIL:                                         FAX:

NAME:                                          HOME:

ADDRESS:                                        CELL/PAGER:

                                               OFFICE:

E-MAIL:                                         FAX:

NAME:                                          HOME:

ADDRESS:                                        CELL/PAGER:

                                               OFFICE:

E-MAIL:                                         FAX:

TIME'S TRUE MEASURE OF VALUE IS DISCOVERED

NOT IN ITS DURATION, BUT IN THE SHARING OF ITS MOMENTS.

NAME:                                           HOME:

ADDRESS:                                         CELL/PAGER:

                                                 OFFICE:

E-MAIL:                                          FAX:

NAME:                                           HOME:

ADDRESS:                                         CELL/PAGER:

                                                 OFFICE:

E-MAIL:                                          FAX:

NAME:                                           HOME:

ADDRESS:                                         CELL/PAGER:

                                                 OFFICE:

E-MAIL:                                          FAX:

NAME:                                           HOME:

ADDRESS:                                         CELL/PAGER:

                                                 OFFICE:

E-MAIL:                                          FAX:

NAME:                                           HOME:

ADDRESS:                                         CELL/PAGER:

                                                 OFFICE:

E-MAIL:                                          FAX:

NAME:                                              HOME:

ADDRESS:                                           CELL/PAGER:

                                                   OFFICE:

E-MAIL:                                            FAX:

NAME:                                              HOME:

ADDRESS:                                           CELL/PAGER:

                                                   OFFICE:

E-MAIL:                                            FAX:

NAME:                                              HOME:

ADDRESS:                                           CELL/PAGER:

                                                   OFFICE:

E-MAIL:                                            FAX:

NAME:                                              HOME:

ADDRESS:                                           CELL/PAGER:

                                                   OFFICE:

E-MAIL:                                            FAX:

NAME:                                              HOME:

ADDRESS:                                           CELL/PAGER:

                                                   OFFICE:

E-MAIL:                                            FAX:

NAME:

ADDRESS:

E-MAIL:

HOME:

CELL/PAGER:

OFFICE:

FAX:

NAME:

ADDRESS:

E-MAIL:

HOME:

CELL/PAGER:

OFFICE:

FAX:

NAME:

ADDRESS:

E-MAIL:

HOME:

CELL/PAGER:

OFFICE:

FAX:

NAME:

ADDRESS:

E-MAIL:

HOME:

CELL/PAGER:

OFFICE:

FAX:

NAME:

ADDRESS:

E-MAIL:

HOME:

CELL/PAGER:

OFFICE:

FAX:

TIME MAY BE FLEETING, BUT THE WARMTH

OF HUMAN EXPERIENCE ENDURES.

NAME:                                          HOME:

ADDRESS:                                       CELL/PAGER:

                                               OFFICE:

E-MAIL:                                        FAX:

NAME:                                          HOME:

ADDRESS:                                       CELL/PAGER:

                                               OFFICE:

E-MAIL:                                        FAX:

NAME:                                          HOME:

ADDRESS:                                       CELL/PAGER:

                                               OFFICE:

E-MAIL:                                        FAX:

NAME:                                          HOME:

ADDRESS:                                       CELL/PAGER:

                                               OFFICE:

E-MAIL:                                        FAX:

NAME:                                          HOME:

ADDRESS:                                       CELL/PAGER:

                                               OFFICE:

E-MAIL:                                        FAX:

NAME:                                          HOME:

ADDRESS:                                       CELL/PAGER:

                                               OFFICE:

E-MAIL:                                         FAX:

NAME:                                          HOME:

ADDRESS:                                       CELL/PAGER:

                                               OFFICE:

E-MAIL:                                         FAX:

NAME:                                          HOME:

ADDRESS:                                       CELL/PAGER:

                                               OFFICE:

E-MAIL:                                         FAX:

NAME:                                          HOME:

ADDRESS:                                       CELL/PAGER:

                                               OFFICE:

E-MAIL:                                         FAX:

NAME:                                          HOME:

ADDRESS:                                       CELL/PAGER:

                                               OFFICE:

E-MAIL:                                         FAX:

NAME:                                          HOME:

ADDRESS:                                       CELL/PAGER:

                                               OFFICE:

E-MAIL:                                         FAX:

NAME:                                          HOME:

ADDRESS:                                       CELL/PAGER:

                                               OFFICE:

E-MAIL:                                         FAX:

NAME:                                          HOME:

ADDRESS:                                       CELL/PAGER:

                                               OFFICE:

E-MAIL:                                         FAX:

NAME:                                          HOME:

ADDRESS:                                       CELL/PAGER:

                                               OFFICE:

E-MAIL:                                         FAX:

NAME:                                          HOME:

ADDRESS:                                       CELL/PAGER:

                                               OFFICE:

E-MAIL:                                         FAX:

SOUL MATES CELEBRATE THE ESSENCE OF WHO WE ARE

AND HAVE FAITH IN ALL THAT WE MAY BECOME.

NAME:                                        HOME:

ADDRESS:                                     CELL/PAGER:

                                             OFFICE:

E-MAIL:                                       FAX:

NAME:                                        HOME:

ADDRESS:                                     CELL/PAGER:

                                             OFFICE:

E-MAIL:                                       FAX:

NAME:                                        HOME:

ADDRESS:                                     CELL/PAGER:

                                             OFFICE:

E-MAIL:                                       FAX:

NAME:                                        HOME:

ADDRESS:                                     CELL/PAGER:

                                             OFFICE:

E-MAIL:                                       FAX:

NAME:                                        HOME:

ADDRESS:                                     CELL/PAGER:

                                             OFFICE:

E-MAIL:                                       FAX:

NAME:

ADDRESS:

EMAIL:

HOME:

CELL/PAGER:

OFFICE:

FAX:

NAME:

ADDRESS:

EMAIL:

HOME:

CELL/PAGER:

OFFICE:

FAX:

NAME:

ADDRESS:

EMAIL:

HOME:

CELL/PAGER:

OFFICE:

FAX:

NAME:

ADDRESS:

EMAIL:

HOME:

CELL/PAGER:

OFFICE:

FAX:

NAME:

ADDRESS:

EMAIL:

HOME:

CELL/PAGER:

OFFICE:

FAX:

NAME:                                    HOME:

ADDRESS:                                 CELL/PAGER:

                                         OFFICE:

E-MAIL:                                  FAX:

NAME:                                    HOME:

ADDRESS:                                 CELL/PAGER:

                                         OFFICE:

E-MAIL:                                  FAX:

NAME:                                    HOME:

ADDRESS:                                 CELL/PAGER:

                                         OFFICE:

E-MAIL:                                  FAX:

NAME:                                    HOME:

ADDRESS:                                 CELL/PAGER:

                                         OFFICE:

E-MAIL:                                  FAX:

NAME:                                    HOME:

ADDRESS:                                 CELL/PAGER:

                                         OFFICE:

E-MAIL:                                  FAX:

*UNDERSTANDING LIFE IS LESS IMPORTANT THAN*

*BELIEVING IN THE GIFTS THAT IT BRINGS.*

NAME: Mary Ann and Harry Power
ADDRESS: 8 Chil Son Avenue
Mansfield, MA 02048
E-MAIL:

HOME: (508) 339-2138
CELL/PAGER:
OFFICE:
FAX:

NAME:
ADDRESS:
E-MAIL:

HOME:
CELL/PAGER:
OFFICE:
FAX:

NAME:
ADDRESS:
E-MAIL:

HOME:
CELL/PAGER:
OFFICE:
FAX:

NAME:
ADDRESS:
E-MAIL:

HOME:
CELL/PAGER:
OFFICE:
FAX:

NAME:
ADDRESS:
E-MAIL:

HOME:
CELL/PAGER:
OFFICE:
FAX:

NAME:

ADDRESS:

E-MAIL:

HOME:

CELL/PAGER:

OFFICE:

FAX:

NAME:

ADDRESS:

E-MAIL:

HOME:

CELL/PAGER:

OFFICE:

FAX:

NAME:

ADDRESS:

E-MAIL:

HOME:

CELL/PAGER:

OFFICE:

FAX:

NAME:

ADDRESS:

E-MAIL:

HOME:

CELL/PAGER:

OFFICE:

FAX:

NAME:

ADDRESS:

E-MAIL:

HOME:

CELL/PAGER:

OFFICE:

FAX:

NAME:

ADDRESS:

E-MAIL:

HOME:

CELL/PAGER:

OFFICE:

FAX:

NAME:

ADDRESS:

E-MAIL:

HOME:

CELL/PAGER:

OFFICE:

FAX:

NAME:

ADDRESS:

E-MAIL:

HOME:

CELL/PAGER:

OFFICE:

FAX:

NAME:

ADDRESS:

E-MAIL:

HOME:

CELL/PAGER:

OFFICE:

FAX:

NAME:

ADDRESS:

E-MAIL:

HOME:

CELL/PAGER:

OFFICE:

FAX:

LOVE IS ALL AROUND US, JUST WAITING FOR OUR EMBRACE.

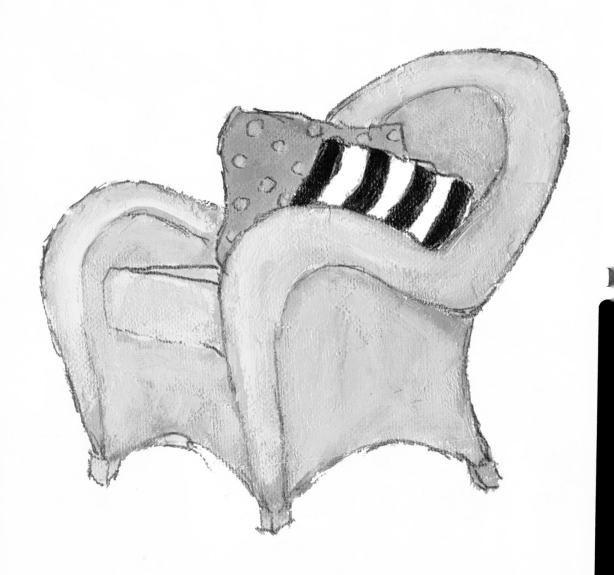

Name:                                     Home:

Address:                             Cell/Pager:

                                            Office:

E-mail:                                   Fax:

Name:                                     Home:

Address:                             Cell/Pager:

                                            Office:

E-mail:                                   Fax:

Name:                                     Home:

Address:                             Cell/Pager:

                                            Office:

E-mail:                                   Fax:

Name:                                     Home:

Address:                             Cell/Pager:

                                            Office:

E-mail:                                   Fax:

Name:                                     Home:

Address:                             Cell/Pager:

                                            Office:

E-mail:                                   Fax:

NAME:                                          HOME:

ADDRESS:                                       CELL/PAGER:

                                               OFFICE:

E-MAIL:                                         FAX:

NAME:                                          HOME:

ADDRESS:                                       CELL/PAGER:

                                               OFFICE:

E-MAIL:                                         FAX:

NAME:                                          HOME:

ADDRESS:                                       CELL/PAGER:

                                               OFFICE:

E-MAIL:                                         FAX:

NAME:                                          HOME:

ADDRESS:                                       CELL/PAGER:

                                               OFFICE:

E-MAIL:                                         FAX:

NAME:                                          HOME:

ADDRESS:                                       CELL/PAGER:

                                               OFFICE:

E-MAIL:                                         FAX:

NAME:                                    HOME:

ADDRESS:                                 CELL/PAGER:

                                         OFFICE:

E-MAIL:                                   FAX:

NAME:                                    HOME:

ADDRESS:                                 CELL/PAGER:

                                         OFFICE:

E-MAIL:                                   FAX:

NAME:                                    HOME:

ADDRESS:                                 CELL/PAGER:

                                         OFFICE:

E-MAIL:                                   FAX:

NAME:                                    HOME:

ADDRESS:                                 CELL/PAGER:

                                         OFFICE:

E-MAIL:                                   FAX:

NAME:                                    HOME:

ADDRESS:                                 CELL/PAGER:

                                         OFFICE:

E-MAIL:                                   FAX:

SOME PEOPLE MOVE OUR SOULS TO SING AND MAKE OUR SPIRITS DANCE.

S

NAME:                                           HOME:

ADDRESS:                                        CELL/PAGER:

                                                OFFICE:

E-MAIL:                                         FAX:

NAME:                                           HOME:

ADDRESS:                                        CELL/PAGER:

                                                OFFICE:

E-MAIL:                                         FAX:

NAME:                                           HOME:

ADDRESS:                                        CELL/PAGER:

                                                OFFICE:

E-MAIL:                                         FAX:

NAME:                                           HOME:

ADDRESS:                                        CELL/PAGER:

                                                OFFICE:

E-MAIL:                                         FAX:

NAME:                                           HOME:

ADDRESS:                                        CELL/PAGER:

                                                OFFICE:

E-MAIL:                                         FAX:

NAME:                                         HOME:

ADDRESS:                                      CELL/PAGER:

                                              OFFICE:

E-MAIL:                                       FAX:

NAME:                                         HOME:

ADDRESS:                                      CELL/PAGER:

                                              OFFICE:

E-MAIL:                                       FAX:

NAME:                                         HOME:

ADDRESS:                                      CELL/PAGER:

                                              OFFICE:

E-MAIL:                                       FAX:

NAME:                                         HOME:

ADDRESS:                                      CELL/PAGER:

                                              OFFICE:

E-MAIL:                                       FAX:

NAME:                                         HOME:

ADDRESS:                                      CELL/PAGER:

                                              OFFICE:

E-MAIL:                                       FAX:

NAME:                                         HOME:

ADDRESS:                             CELL/PAGER:

OFFICE:

E-MAIL:                                      FAX:

NAME:                                          HOME:

ADDRESS:                             CELL/PAGER:

OFFICE:

E-MAIL:                                      FAX:

NAME:                                          HOME:

ADDRESS:                             CELL/PAGER:

OFFICE:

E-MAIL:                                      FAX:

NAME:                                          HOME:

ADDRESS:                             CELL/PAGER:

OFFICE:

E-MAIL:                                      FAX:

NAME:                                          HOME:

ADDRESS:                             CELL/PAGER:

OFFICE:

E-MAIL:                                      FAX:

ALL THAT WE VALUE IN LIFE IS MEASURED WITH A SACRED

REVERENCE IN HONOR OF LOVE AND KINSHIP.

NAME:                                          HOME:

ADDRESS:                                       CELL/PAGER:

                                               OFFICE:

E-MAIL:                                         FAX:

NAME:                                          HOME:

ADDRESS:                                       CELL/PAGER:

                                               OFFICE:

E-MAIL:                                         FAX:

NAME:                                          HOME:

ADDRESS:                                       CELL/PAGER:

                                               OFFICE:

E-MAIL:                                         FAX:

NAME:                                          HOME:

ADDRESS:                                       CELL/PAGER:

                                               OFFICE:

E-MAIL:                                         FAX:

NAME:                                          HOME:

ADDRESS:                                       CELL/PAGER:

                                               OFFICE:

E-MAIL:                                         FAX:

NAME:                                              HOME:

ADDRESS:                                           CELL/PAGER:

                                                   OFFICE:

E-MAIL:                                            FAX:

NAME:                                              HOME:

ADDRESS:                                           CELL/PAGER:

                                                   OFFICE:

E-MAIL:                                            FAX:

NAME:                                              HOME:

ADDRESS:                                           CELL/PAGER:

                                                   OFFICE:

E-MAIL:                                            FAX:

NAME:                                              HOME:

ADDRESS:                                           CELL/PAGER:

                                                   OFFICE:

E-MAIL:                                            FAX:

NAME:                                              HOME:

ADDRESS:                                           CELL/PAGER:

                                                   OFFICE:

E-MAIL:                                            FAX:

NAME:

ADDRESS:

E-MAIL:

HOME:

CELL/PAGER:

OFFICE:

FAX:

NAME:

ADDRESS:

E-MAIL:

HOME:

CELL/PAGER:

OFFICE:

FAX:

NAME:

ADDRESS:

E-MAIL:

HOME:

CELL/PAGER:

OFFICE:

FAX:

NAME:

ADDRESS:

E-MAIL:

HOME:

CELL/PAGER:

OFFICE:

FAX:

NAME:

ADDRESS:

E-MAIL:

HOME:

CELL/PAGER:

OFFICE:

FAX:

SOME PEOPLE ARE BEACONS OF HOPE. THEIR SHINING

BELIEF IN US HELPS US TO BELIEVE IN OURSELVES.

U
V

NAME:                                        HOME:

ADDRESS:                                     CELL/PAGER:

                                             OFFICE:

E-MAIL:                                      FAX:

NAME:                                        HOME:

ADDRESS:                                     CELL/PAGER:

                                             OFFICE:

E-MAIL:                                      FAX:

NAME:                                        HOME:

ADDRESS:                                     CELL/PAGER:

                                             OFFICE:

E-MAIL:                                      FAX:

NAME:                                        HOME:

ADDRESS:                                     CELL/PAGER:

                                             OFFICE:

E-MAIL:                                      FAX:

NAME:                                        HOME:

ADDRESS:                                     CELL/PAGER:

                                             OFFICE:

E-MAIL:                                      FAX:

NAME:

ADDRESS:

E-MAIL:

HOME:

CELL/PAGER:

OFFICE:

FAX:

NAME:

ADDRESS:

E-MAIL:

HOME:

CELL/PAGER:

OFFICE:

FAX:

NAME:

ADDRESS:

E-MAIL:

HOME:

CELL/PAGER:

OFFICE:

FAX:

NAME:

ADDRESS:

E-MAIL:

HOME:

CELL/PAGER:

OFFICE:

FAX:

NAME:

ADDRESS:

E-MAIL:

HOME:

CELL/PAGER:

OFFICE:

FAX:

NAME:

ADDRESS:

E-MAIL:

HOME:

CELL/PAGER:

OFFICE:

FAX:

NAME:

ADDRESS:

E-MAIL:

HOME:

CELL/PAGER:

OFFICE:

FAX:

NAME:

ADDRESS:

E-MAIL:

HOME:

CELL/PAGER:

OFFICE:

FAX:

NAME:

ADDRESS:

E-MAIL:

HOME:

CELL/PAGER:

OFFICE:

FAX:

NAME:

ADDRESS:

E-MAIL:

HOME:

CELL/PAGER:

OFFICE:

FAX:

TO BELIEVE IS TO TRUST IN THE MIRACLE OF LIVING

AND IN THE BEAUTY OF ONE ANOTHER.

W

NAME:                                          HOME:

ADDRESS:                                       CELL/PAGER:

                                               OFFICE:

E-MAIL:                                         FAX:

NAME:                                          HOME:

ADDRESS:                                       CELL/PAGER:

                                               OFFICE:

E-MAIL:                                         FAX:

NAME:                                          HOME:

ADDRESS:                                       CELL/PAGER:

                                               OFFICE:

E-MAIL:                                         FAX:

NAME:                                          HOME:

ADDRESS:                                       CELL/PAGER:

                                               OFFICE:

E-MAIL:                                         FAX:

NAME:                                          HOME:

ADDRESS:                                       CELL/PAGER:

                                               OFFICE:

E-MAIL:                                         FAX:

NAME:                                    HOME:

ADDRESS:                                 CELL/PAGER:

                                         OFFICE:

E-MAIL:                                  FAX:

NAME:                                    HOME:

ADDRESS:                                 CELL/PAGER:

                                         OFFICE:

E-MAIL:                                  FAX:

NAME:                                    HOME:

ADDRESS:                                 CELL/PAGER:

                                         OFFICE:

E-MAIL:                                  FAX:

NAME:                                    HOME:

ADDRESS:                                 CELL/PAGER:

                                         OFFICE:

E-MAIL:                                  FAX:

NAME:                                    HOME:

ADDRESS:                                 CELL/PAGER:

                                         OFFICE:

E-MAIL:                                  FAX:

NAME:

ADDRESS:

E-MAIL:

HOME:

CELL/PAGER:

OFFICE:

FAX:

NAME:

ADDRESS:

E-MAIL:

HOME:

CELL/PAGER:

OFFICE:

FAX:

NAME:

ADDRESS:

E-MAIL:

HOME:

CELL/PAGER:

OFFICE:

FAX:

NAME:

ADDRESS:

E-MAIL:

HOME:

CELL/PAGER:

OFFICE:

FAX:

NAME:

ADDRESS:

E-MAIL:

HOME:

CELL/PAGER:

OFFICE:

FAX:

REMEMBER EVERYTHING.

XYZ

NAME:                                          HOME:

ADDRESS:                                       CELL/PAGER:

                                               OFFICE:

E-MAIL:                                         FAX:

NAME:                                          HOME:

ADDRESS:                                       CELL/PAGER:

                                               OFFICE:

E-MAIL:                                         FAX:

NAME:                                          HOME:

ADDRESS:                                       CELL/PAGER:

                                               OFFICE:

E-MAIL:                                         FAX:

NAME:                                          HOME:

ADDRESS:                                       CELL/PAGER:

                                               OFFICE:

E-MAIL:                                         FAX:

NAME:                                          HOME:

ADDRESS:                                       CELL/PAGER:

                                               OFFICE:

E-MAIL:                                         FAX:

NAME:                                    HOME:

ADDRESS:                                 CELL/PAGER:

                                         OFFICE:

E-MAIL:                                  FAX:

NAME:                                    HOME:

ADDRESS:                                 CELL/PAGER:

                                         OFFICE:

E-MAIL:                                  FAX:

NAME:                                    HOME:

ADDRESS:                                 CELL/PAGER:

                                         OFFICE:

E-MAIL:                                  FAX:

NAME:                                    HOME:

ADDRESS:                                 CELL/PAGER:

                                         OFFICE:

E-MAIL:                                  FAX:

NAME:                                    HOME:

ADDRESS:                                 CELL/PAGER:

                                         OFFICE:

E-MAIL:                                  FAX:

Flavia

Lisa and her daughter Sylvie

Flavia Weedn is one of America's leading inspirational writers and illustrators. Her work, and the work of her daughter and co-author, Lisa Weedn, celebrates life and offers hope to the human spirit. Their collaborative work has touched the lives of millions through books, cards, posters, fine stationery products, and hundreds of licensed goods throughout the world.

Flavia and Lisa live in Santa Barbara, California.